This book belongs to...

Why?
A Sciencey, Rhymey Guide to Rainbows

An original concept by author Billy Dunne

© Billy Dunne

Illustrated by Rhys Jefferys

MAVERICK ARTS PUBLISHING LTD
Studio 11, City Business Centre, 6 Brighton Road, Horsham,
West Sussex, RH13 5BB, +44 (0)1403 256941
© Maverick Arts Publishing Limited 2020
Published October 2020

A CIP catalogue record for this book
is available at the British Library.

ISBN 978-1-84886-487-0

Maverick
publishing

www.maverickbooks.co.uk

$$\left(v_{ph}^2 \nabla^2 - \frac{\partial^2}{\partial t^2} \right) E = 0$$

$$\left(v_{ph}^2 \nabla^2 - \frac{\partial^2}{\partial t^2} \right) B =$$

$$\nabla \cdot E = 0$$

$$\nabla \times E = -\frac{\partial B}{\partial t}$$

$$\nabla \cdot B = 0$$

$$\nabla \times B = \mu_0 \varepsilon_0 \frac{\partial E}{\partial t}$$

Why?

By **Billy Dunne**

Ilustrated by **Rhys Jefferys**

"What a lovely day!" said Dad,
a **rainbow** overhead.
"You get them when the rain has passed,
and sunshine comes instead."

His daughter stared with wonder at the **rainbow** in the sky.
She looked her daddy in the eyes, and softly asked him, **"Why?"**

"The **colours** in a beam of light
are jumbled up together,
but **split** apart when passing through
a spot of rainy weather."

Red
Orange
Yellow
Green
Blue
Indigo
Violet

Her dad was rather pleased with that,
and started walking by.

Until his daughter made him stop,
by simply asking, **"Why?"**

Beam of light

"When light encounters water,
from the rain that came before.
The **red** light bends a little bit,
the **blue** a little more."

Her daddy eyed her nervously,
awaiting her reply.

His darling daughter clapped her hands,
intently asking, **"Why?"**

Red

Blue

Beam of light

"Well, water's made of **atoms** which are bunched up rather tightly. It really **slows** the blue light down; the red light, only slightly."

Her daddy wiped his sweating head,
she looked him in the eye.

With growing passion in her voice,
she asked intently, **"Why?"**

depends upon the **wavelength** of the colour of the light."

Blue

Indigo

Violet

Collapsing in a nervous heap,
and trying not to cry,
her anxious daddy rocked himself.
His daughter pressed him, **"Why?"**

"The complex **composition** of the photon quantum field, describes the interaction that the **rainbow** has revealed."

$$\left(v_{ph}^2 \nabla^2 - \frac{\partial^2}{\partial t^2} \right) E = 0$$

$$\left(v_{ph}^2 \nabla^2 - \frac{\partial^2}{\partial t^2} \right) B = 0$$

$$\nabla \cdot E = 0$$

$$\nabla \times E = -\frac{\partial B}{\partial t}$$

$$\nabla \cdot B = 0$$

$$\nabla \times B = \mu_0 \epsilon_0 \frac{\partial E}{\partial t}$$

$$\sqrt{x^2}$$

She crawled beside her sobbing dad,
her hand upon his head.
And whispered with a loving voice,
"You could have...

„simply said..."